# BEEKEE...

*for*
## BEGINNERS

## The Kitchen Garden

*By the same Author.*
*In the same series:*
Food from the Kitchen Garden
Keeping a Few Hens in your Garden
Keeping a Few Ducks in your Garden
A Peacock on the Lawn (with S. Carpenter)
Goose on the Green
*Also:*
The Big Book of Garden Hens
A Henkeeper's Journal
A Christmas Journal

Edited by Francine Raymond
Published by the Kitchen Garden
Church Lane, Troston
Bury St Edmunds Suffolk IP31 1EX
Tel 01359 268 322
Email: francine@jfraymond.demon.co.uk
www.kitchen-garden-hens.co.uk

ISBN 0-9532857-2-3

Printed in Suffolk, England

With thanks to: Philip and Valerie Scoles, Jo Kendall,
Jean-François Raymond and Alice Wooledge Salmon.

'What living creature can you keep about you that yields more pleasure, delight and profit, than these that possess so little room as a small part of your garden.'
*John Worlidge 1677.*

## Introduction
Do you dream of a cottage garden with pretty white beehives and bees humming gently as they weave among the roses and lavender? Is there a jar of homemade honey on the table and does the house smell of beeswax polish?

This is where the dream usually fades. In real life, books on beekeeping - even those for beginners are unnecessarily complicated; there's a frightening mystique surrounding the life cycle and habits of the honey bee; a whole new language to master and much talk of disease - varroa and foul brood - and worse.

Keeping bees is really quite simple. You start with a hive and find yourself a mentor - someone who will hold your hand and help you through the first twelve months. Then you'll find you have painlessly learned the cycle of the beekeeper's year and are rewarded with several jars of delicious honey on the larder shelf. Your garden will benefit enormously from the presence of pollinating bees - I have doubled the harvest from my orchard.

Of course you don't need a country garden either, there are many successful urban beekeepers. The mixed plants in city gardens and parks make delicate honey and there's more variety in town than in the countryside where bees forage single-crop fields. There are even beehives on the flat roofs of office blocks and schools in central London.

Remember, the bees do most of the work for you. You, as their custodian have just three tasks: to encourage the bees to make and store the honey that you extract, to discourage swarming and to coddle them during the cold winter months.

That's it really. So how do you start?

## Getting Started

The first thing you need is a friend or mentor - an experienced beekeeper who will guide you and introduce a whole honeycomb of friendly amateurs. Beekeepers are generous with advice, equipment and will be a source of bees and secondhand paraphenalia. By chance I met my mentor Philip Scoles - from whom I've learned almost everything I know - through the secretary of my local beekeeping society, so I suggest you contact your branch (see page 32).

## Equipment
### Hive

Next you will need a hive or better, two. There are two kinds: the WBC, most people's idea of the traditional white beehive: pretty in the garden, easy for beginners and 'good for lady beekeepers', and the National hive. This is a square, brown box. It has light, single walls, is inexpensive and easy to move around - the choice of most professional beekeepers - though some admit the WBC hive's double walls help to keep the bees snug in Winter and cool in Summer.

# The Hive Layout

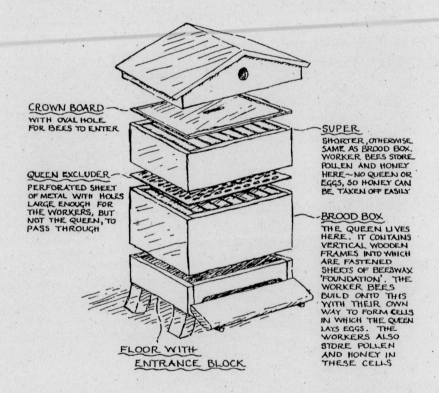

CROWN BOARD
WITH OVAL HOLE
FOR BEES TO ENTER

QUEEN EXCLUDER
PERFORATED SHEET
OF METAL WITH HOLES
LARGE ENOUGH FOR
THE WORKERS, BUT
NOT THE QUEEN, TO
PASS THROUGH

SUPER
SHORTER, OTHERWISE
SAME AS BROOD BOX.
WORKER BEES STORE
POLLEN AND HONEY
HERE ~ NO QUEEN OR
EGGS, SO HONEY CAN
BE TAKEN OFF EASILY

BROOD BOX
THE QUEEN LIVES
HERE. IT CONTAINS
VERTICAL WOODEN
FRAMES INTO WHICH
ARE FASTENED
SHEETS OF BEESWAX
'FOUNDATION'. THE
WORKER BEES
BUILD ONTO THIS
WITH THEIR OWN
WAY TO FORM CELLS
IN WHICH THE QUEEN
LAYS EGGS. THE
WORKERS ALSO
STORE POLLEN
AND HONEY IN
THESE CELLS

FLOOR WITH
ENTRANCE BLOCK

## Smoker

An essential piece of equipment. Smoke puffed into a hive makes bees drowsy and easy to handle. It doesn't anaesthetize the bees but signals danger and makes them rush to their honey stores and gorge themselves with food. After about three minutes they will be replete, sleepy and less likely to sting. You can open the hive and work, giving extra puffs occasionally. Your mentor will show you how the smoker works, but I rather like the modern spray smokers.

## Hive Tool

The beekeeper's Swiss Army knife, a vital tool used for many tasks, especially lifting and moving frames.

## Clothing

The best outfit for dealing with bees consists of a completely protective all-in-one boiler suit with an integral hood, vizor or veil; wellies to tuck over your trouser ends, and long fine rubber or leather gloves. All these should be white. Bees are very sensitive to colour, preferring certain coloured flowers, but they find white most soothing and will be calm and less likely to sting. They don't like brown.

This is your starter kit. It can be bought new from the suppliers listed on the final page of this book, but can be found secondhand through your local beekeeper's association. Don't skimp on clothing though, as a beginner you need to feel confident that you will not be stung.

## Getting your bees

Now you're ready for the bees. You could wait for a swarm, but this is an unreliable source and you won't know their mettle. Some gentlemen keepers take a macho pride in managing a fiercely bad-tempered swarm, which they boast produces more honey. I prefer a gentler strain of bee. It's best to start with a 'nuc' - a nuclear colony - from an experienced beekeeper. A 'nuc' is a frame full of worker bees, egg cells, developing grubs and most importantly, a queen. They could be from a named strain, New Zealand perhaps - special gentle bees. I started with a New Zealand queen and a 'nuc' from Philip's hive and now have some Buckfast Abbey bees, famous for their tranquility and hardiness - which they need to survive our cruel East Anglian winters. In any case, discuss this with your mentor.

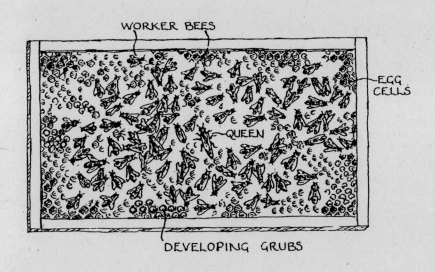

WORKER BEES

EGG CELLS

QUEEN

DEVELOPING GRUBS

## Stings

Now we should touch on the painful topic of bee stings. If you have ever had an allergic reaction to honey bee venom, abandon the dream of keeping bees now. Further stings will only make the problem worse, and although a doctor can give you a course of de-sensitizing injections, it may not be worth the pain.

Being stung is probably what puts most people off keeping bees. If you are well protected you will rarely be hurt and knowing this will give you the confidence to handle your bees calmly. In turn, this reassures your bees and they will be less likely to sting. I talk to mine gently all the time, it helps, I'm sure.

If you *are* unlucky, quickly remove the sting with a small knife - beekeepers use their hive tool. You'll see a small pink mark with a black point in the middle. Scrape the blade towards the sting until it pops out and then rub a little anti-histamine cream on the spot to soothe soreness. If you are stung on the face, particularly near the eyes or inside your mouth, remove the sting straight away and go to the doctor because the soft tissue will swell up alarmingly (as I can vouch after a week looking like the Elephant Man).

## Keeping Notes

Make a record of all you do and when. You can learn by looking back. Some beekeepers put a postcard inside the hive with a shorthand account of all they've done, but the bees nibble the card and I can't read my scribble written wearing gloves. I keep my notes in a diary next to my gardening jottings, but promise to keep a special Beekeeper's Journal next year. Who knows, it may be useful to other beekeepers as well.

## Gardening with Bees

Bees will forage wherever there's food, in fields, parks, hedgerows or next door's garden, but they appreciate certain plants near to hand at times when there's a shortage: - early pulmonarias, Spring fruit blossom and late ivy flowers just before hibernation. I will mention their favourite plants and the ones that make good honey as we go through the beekeeper's year together. If you have to spray your garden at all, always do it at night when the bees are in their hive.

# The Honey Bees' Year

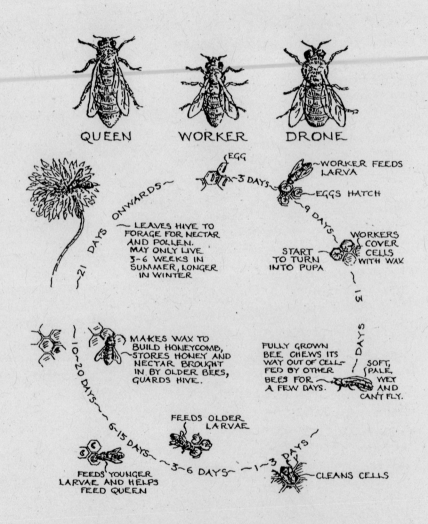

QUEEN    WORKER    DRONE

EGG

~3 DAYS~

~WORKER FEEDS LARVA

~EGGS HATCH

~9 DAYS~

WORKERS COVER CELLS WITH WAX

~21 DAYS ONWARDS~

~ LEAVES HIVE TO FORAGE FOR NECTAR AND POLLEN. MAY ONLY LIVE 3-6 WEEKS IN SUMMER, LONGER IN WINTER

START TO TURN INTO PUPA

~13 DAYS~

MAKES WAX TO BUILD HONEYCOMB, STORES HONEY AND NECTAR BROUGHT IN BY OLDER BEES, GUARDS HIVE.

FULLY GROWN BEE CHEWS ITS WAY OUT OF CELL FED BY OTHER BEES FOR A FEW DAYS.

SOFT, PALE, WET AND CAN'T FLY.

~10-20 DAYS~

~6-15 DAYS~

FEEDS OLDER LARVAE

~3-6 DAYS~    ~1-3 DAYS~

CLEANS CELLS

FEEDS YOUNGER LARVAE AND HELPS FEED QUEEN

14

## The Beekeeper's Year
## Spring

It's mid February and there's welcome warmth in the sun, the thrush is singing and the snowdrops, aconites and crocuses are flowering under the trees. As I pass the apricot tree that hugs the herb garden wall, I can see a honeybee working on the blossom. I rush down the path to the beehives in the orchard and I'm thrilled to see my bees flying in and out of the hives - they have survived the winter. I must fill the feeder with sugar syrup because nectar is still scarce and I'll leave their blanket on until April when I open the hive.

Time to get ready for *your* bees. New beehives can be set up straight away, but if yours is secondhand, give it a thorough scrape and repaint to destroy diseases and remove wax and propolis - the sticky bee glue. WBC hives may need a coat of white paint and a new felt roof. Site your hives carefully. Choose a warm, sheltered south facing spot with a clear flight path to the hive entrance and with no overhanging trees or high walls. A brick or paving base will keep the hives and your feet dry.

You and your mentor are ready for your 'nuc'. Place the frame containing the worker bees and brood (their eggs and grubs) in the centre of the brood box. The queen will arrive separately, as befits her station, so have a good look at her before you pop her in the hive. Ask your mentor to mark her head with a coloured felt tip pen, so you'll know her in future. She is larger and more elegant than her workers with a pointed *derriere* and a sting reserved for other queens.

Put the queen in a small plastic container, block the entrance with a boiled sweet and place it in the middle of the brood chamber. By the time the workers have eaten their way through the sweet, they will have grown accustomed to her smell and accepted her as their queen. She will immediately start laying eggs.

From now on your bees will make honey so develop a regular routine inspecting *every week* from mid April till autumn when the hive is closed. Only procrastinate if the weather is bad. Your mentor will do this first time round. Watch carefully. Put on the protective outfit making sure there are no gaps at neck, wrists or ankles.

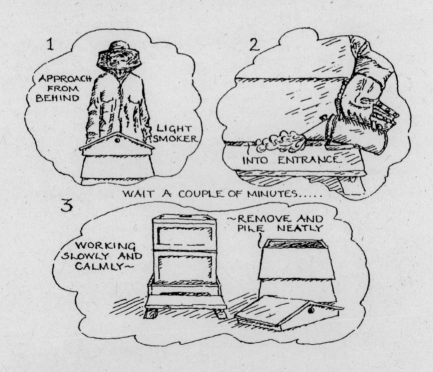

The outside frames will often be empty, but in the middle you'll see cells filled with honey or capped with wax. Some may be filled with pollen and some with sealed or unsealed grubs. Others will seem empty, but look carefully and you'll see eggs like tiny pieces of white thread standing upright at first, then turning on their side. If you look at the outer combs in the nest you'll see cells with domed caps, these are the drone larvae, bigger and squarer than the workers; their sole purpose in life is to impregnate young queens. They don't sting.

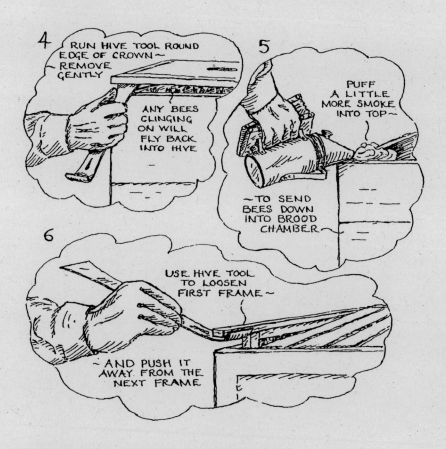

4 RUN HIVE TOOL ROUND EDGE OF CROWN ~ REMOVE GENTLY

ANY BEES CLINGING ON WILL FLY BACK INTO HIVE

5 PUFF A LITTLE MORE SMOKE INTO TOP ~

~ TO SEND BEES DOWN INTO BROOD CHAMBER ~

6 USE HIVE TOOL TO LOOSEN FIRST FRAME ~

~ AND PUSH IT AWAY FROM THE NEXT FRAME

The queen holds court in the centre of the nest, easily recognizable by her coloured dot and surrounded by her workers. Learn to spot the new queen cells, which are larger, pointed and often hidden in corners; your mentor will point them out. Destroy them by squashing them with the hive tool, or your bees will swarm. Checking regularly will stop this happening.

By the end of April, as the outer frames of the brood box fill with honey or brood, put in a *super*. This is a shallow box of frames placed on top of the brood box, separated by a queen excluder, so that she can carry on laying eggs in her box while the workers store the honey in the super. This way you can remove the super when it's full of honey without disturbing the queen.

Take time to learn from your mentor about the layout of the hive, to recognize its inhabitants and to seek and destroy the dreaded queen cells.

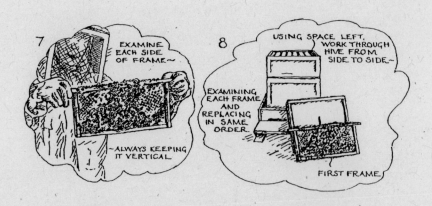

# The Queen's Cycle

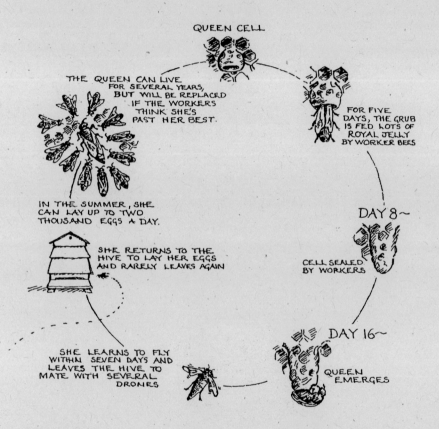

QUEEN CELL

THE QUEEN CAN LIVE FOR SEVERAL YEARS, BUT WILL BE REPLACED IF THE WORKERS THINK SHE'S PAST HER BEST.

FOR FIVE DAYS, THE GRUB IS FED LOTS OF ROYAL JELLY BY WORKER BEES

IN THE SUMMER, SHE CAN LAY UP TO TWO THOUSAND EGGS A DAY.

DAY 8~

SHE RETURNS TO THE HIVE TO LAY HER EGGS AND RARELY LEAVES AGAIN

CELL SEALED BY WORKERS

DAY 16~

SHE LEARNS TO FLY WITHIN SEVEN DAYS AND LEAVES THE HIVE TO MATE WITH SEVERAL DRONES

QUEEN EMERGES

## Valerie's Plain Honey Cake

Valerie is Philip's wife and she gave me her precious recipe for this easy cake that everyone loves.

| | |
|---|---|
| 4oz soft light brown sugar | 1 tab water |
| 5oz unsalted butter | 2 freerange eggs |
| 6oz honey | 7 oz sifted self raising flour |

7" or 8" tin, greased and lined with baking parchment.

Melt the sugar, butter, honey and water in a medium saucepan stirring over a moderate heat till dissolved. Whisk in the beaten eggs and the flour till smooth.

Pour into the tin and bake in a moderate oven (180C/350F) for an hour until a skewer comes out clean. Leave to cool before turning out. The cake can be topped with lemon icing or decorated with sliced preserved ginger and served warm with crème fraiche.

## Summer

Hot, drowsy summer days with the scent of herbs, honeysuckle and lavender seducing the bees from plant to plant with heady smells and tempting nectar. Beekeepers talk rapturously about the 'flow' of honey and you will learn to recognize the signs. You'll see lines of bees flying determinedly back and forth from the hive and when you look inside, the super will be filling up. Leave it until the cells have all been capped

We'll deal with extracting honey in the next chapter but if you have over-wintered a colony you may get some reward in early summer. If your bees have made a beeline for bright yellow rapeflowers, there will be pots of creamy rather bland honey, but if they have foraged in gardens and orchards you may be lucky and get a little of the pale gold delicate ambrosia I call Spring Blossom honey. It is delicious.

Busy times for beekeepers. Hives must be inspected weekly, supers added or removed and queen cells destroyed. The colony is multiplying; the queen can lay up to 2000 eggs a day and you'll see bees everywhere. Too many and the queen and half her subjects will swarm and leave the hive.

The first sign is a rather frightening, angry buzzing. Scout bees will scour the garden for a new home - the corner of a shed, barn, a dead tree trunk or if you're lucky, the spare hive. They will be followed by a dark mass the size of a rugby football with the queen in the middle of the scrum. It's an awesome sight and a quick phone call to your mentor would be a good idea. Put on your protective clothing but don't panic - bees rarely sting while they are swarming, they're much too busy looking for a new home.

If the swarm disappears next door or further, visit your neighbours and tell them what you are doing. Try to sound confident (hopefully you'll have introduced yourself previously wearing a more conformist outfit). Take a skep or sturdy cardboard box and an old sheet. You'll probably find your bees hanging from a branch. Hold the skep under them (you may need a stepladder), give the branch a sharp tap and the swarm should drop into your skep, which you then cover with the sheet. Beware: a swarm is heavier than you think.

Carry the bees to your spare hive and make a bridge of the gap from the sheet to the hive entrance with a small plank. Shake the bees gently on to the sheet and you may feel slightly smug as they make their way up the slope. The new colony will need sugar syrup to feed on until they make their own honey (see page 27).

Now you must deal with the queenless colony left in your original hive. Light the smoker and smoke the hive; open and work methodically through the frames destroying all the queen cells but one. This cell will hatch into your new queen. The rest of the bees will seem aimless, anxious and rather noisy, until the queen hatches 15 days later. At the rather precocious age of five days, she and several drones will leave the hive to mate, coming back five days later to lay eggs. It will take a while for the colony to thrive again and you'll notice a drop in honey yield.

If you don't have a spare hive, ask local beekeepers to find your swarm a home; it's a shame because half your colony and half your honey production will be lost. Try to avoid swarming by examining the hive regularly and spotting the warning signs. Prevent overcrowding by adding new supers and be vigilant - destroy queen cells.

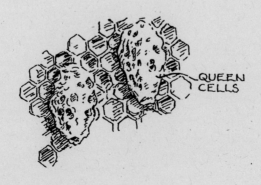

QUEEN
CELLS

### Lavender and Honey Icecream

Treat yourself to this wonderful pudding using your own honey and lavender flowers. Balm for stings and memories of swarms past.

1 pt single cream                               4 freerange egg yolks
4 or 5 lavender spikes                           6 oz honey
¼ pt double cream, greek yoghurt or crème fraiche

Bring the single cream and lavender flowers to boiling point and leave in a warm place to infuse for 1/2 hour. Beat the egg yolks, whisk in the warm cream and strain back into the saucepan, putting the lavender aside. Warm the custard over a low heat, whisking till thick enough to coat the back of a spoon. Stir in the warmed liquid honey. Taste and include the lavender flowers if necessary - freezing will intensify the flavour. Leave the custard to cool and add the whipped double cream or yoghurt or crème fraiche, and remove the lavender. Scoop into your icecream maker and follow instructions. Serve with little biscuits and garnish with fresh lavender flowers. Lovely with strawberries or sliced peaches.

## Autumn

Harvest in the garden, orchard, and in your hives. On warm September days the bees are still working the blackberry flowers, but you can relax, they won't swarm this late in the year. Time for beginners to extract their honey. Decide where you're going to work. Everything will get very sticky, so a washable floor is a must.

Wait till the super is full of honey and all the cells are capped. The day before, put an extra crown board between the brood box and the super, fitted with a bee escape (a one way door that lets the bees into the brood chamber but not back into the super). By the next day they will all have assembled in the chamber.

Your most important piece of equipment is an extractor; try to borrow one first time round. Like a spin dryer holding frames, it throws the honey outwards to run down the sides of the drum, collecting at the base where there is a tap to drain the honey into a filtered tank. Extractors come in various sizes - the electric ones are easiest, but are heavy to lift. Some have integral heaters that are useful for quick-setting honeys, like rapeflower. My favourite is an electric extractor that holds two frames of honey. Light, plastic and shallow, it's easy to clean, but too slow for many hivefulls.

On the great day you and your mentor, clad in protective outfits, smokers puffing, take a wheelbarrow carrying a large washable tray and a soft handbrush out to the hive. After smoking, remove the roof, crownboard and lifts. Starting at one end of the super, remove each frame, brushing any stubborn bees into the hive. As each heavy frame is cleared, manhandle it into the wheelbarrow. Re-assemble the hive and leave the frames of honey on the tray somewhere warm for the night - a greenhouse, boiler room or kitchen.

The next morning uncap the cells of honey by running a bread knife across them. Put the frames in the extractor and switch on. You will hear honey and wax splatter against the walls of the extractor. When the frames are empty, replace with full ones until you have emptied all the frames. Take these outside on the tray to the hive - your bees will finish the washing up.

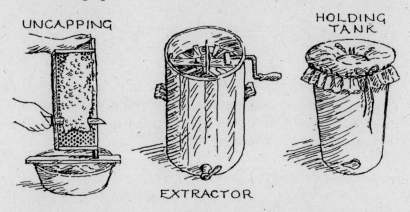

UNCAPPING

HOLDING TANK

EXTRACTOR

When all the honey has collected in the base of the extractor, lift it onto a table and position your holding tank to collect the honey. Cut a piece of muslin larger than the top of the tank and tie it on with string. The muslin should sag slightly. With the tank tap tightly closed, turn on the extractor tap and leave the honey to drip through for twenty four hours and then for another day and night - to clear the air bubbles.

Collect the cappings and any wax from the muslin and filters in a sieve over a basin. The wax can be washed in a bucket with cold water, re-sieved, drained and dried. Melted in an old saucepan over a gentle heat, and filtered through muslin, it can be poured into a tin and will result in a surprisingly small block of pure beeswax.

Decant your honey into glass jars, screw on the lids, wipe clean, stick on some pretty labels with the date and stand back and admire your bees' handiwork. Give an extra round of applause for you and your mentor. Having stolen all the bees' honey, you will now have to replace their winter rations with strong sugar solution. Measure 2lb granulated sugar into a large bowl and dissolve in a pint of boiling water. Leave till cold and pour into a feeder or upturned honey jar with a perforated lid. Check every two or three days. The bees will take this substitute for the jars you have in your larder and store and cap it exactly as they do flower honey.

Before you replace the super, pop in the medicated strips of plastic that kill the Varroa mite. - that nasty little parasite that can destroy a whole colony in time and is the scourge of all beekeepers. Suspend two strips in the brood chamber and leave for 6 weeks.

Your harvest in and your bees safe, the beekeeper's year is almost over. Bake some fresh scones for tea and treat your mentor and family to the first taste of your own honey.

**Partridge with Lemon and Honey**
It's also the game season. This recipe works as well with pheasant or freerange chicken.

| | |
|---|---|
| 1 unwaxed lemon | 4 partridges |
| 2 tabs honey | 8 sprigs thyme |
| 1 tab olive oil | ½ pt chicken or game stock |

Pre-heat the oven to 425F/220C
Grate the lemon zest and squeeze the juice into a bowl. Dissolve the honey over gentle heat and whisk into the lemon juice. Add olive oil, salt, pepper and lemon zest. Put the birds in a deep dish, pour on the marinade and turn the birds till they're well covered. Leave for at least an hour, turning occasionally. Place the partridge in a roasting tin with the marinade and tuck in the thyme. Roast for 20 mins and then turn the birds breast-upwards with half the stock and cook for a further 20 mins. Skewer to check if the juices run clear and leave to rest in a warm place. Deglaze the pan with the remaining stock and strain the gravy. Serve with glossy green watercress and medlar or quince jelly.

## Winter

Quiet times for bees - and beekeepers. During the last pale sunny days of autumn your bees will forage for any nectar they can find among the handsome yellow ivy flowerheads, but as days get shorter and colder they will stay in the hive. The miserable drones are expelled to die of cold - their useful days over. Food stores must be saved for the queen and her workers who form a spherical mass in the middle of the hive, close to the honey store so they can snack quickly without losing body heat.

Do all you can to help your bees survive the winter. The hive entrance must be narrowed with chamfered blocks of wood and a strip of perforated metal is popped in behind to deter any mice who will try and steal the honey while the hive is quiescent. I put a piece of folded blanket on top of the crown board to retain heat. After the bees are put to bed and tucked in, do not disturb them. Never open the hive in cold weather, bees chill very quickly.

Time to take stock, clean and overhaul your equipment, maybe order some new tools and books for the coming season from the list on the last page. Re-cap and remember all you have learnt with your mentor, and wonder if you can face next year's routine alone. Order seeds and plants to tempt your bees especially herbs like hyssop, thyme and borage, or if you need to boost the vitality of your garden, consider planting green manures like clover, alfalfa or phacelia, your bees will love their flowers.

You can make Christmas presents with the honey and beeswax you have produced; candlemaking needs a book of its own, but beeswax cream polish is easy to make, inimitable for preserving furniture and it makes the house smell lovely.

7 ½ oz beeswax                   3 teasp soapflakes
1 ½ pts real turpentine        3 teasp washing soda
1 ½ pts distilled water          ½ teasp ammonia

Put the wax and turps into a big old tin (like a catering size Nescafe tin) and leave to stand in a pan of boiling water until the wax melts. Boil the water, soapflakes, soda and ammonia in an old saucepan and add to the wax mixture, beating with a rotary whisk for 10-15 minutes - jolly hard work. Pour the cooled polish into 5 honey jars and leave until cold. Pop on the lids and label. Can be perfumed with lavender or crushed sweet cicely seeds.

## Granola

When extracting, you will be left with a bowl of honey drippings from the cappings and empty frames. It can be strained and used in recipes, like this one for a delicious, healthy breakfast cereal.

| | |
|---|---|
| 4 cups jumbo oats | 1 teasp ground cinnamon |
| 1 cup pumpkin & sunflower seeds | pinch of salt |
| ½ cup almonds | ½ cup honey |
| ½ cup wheatgerm | 1 teasp pure vanilla extract |
| 1 cup sultanas & chopped apricots | ½ cup sunflower oil |

Mix all the dry ingredients together, apart from the fruit. Whisk the honey, oil and vanilla and add it to the base, stirring till combined. Spread the mixture on a non-stick tray and bake at 350F stirring occasionally until it's a rich even brown. Leave to cool and stir in the fruit. Store in an airtight container and eat at breakfast with milk or yoghurt or use to top an apple puree for a quick pudding.

## USEFUL INFORMATION

British Beekeepers' Association          02476 696679
*They will put you in touch with your local branch.*

### Beekeepers' Supplies

EH Thorne (Beehives) Ltd          01673858555
*For a wide range of equipment and clothing.*
Limetree Apiaries          01422 375713
*For inexpensive clothing.*
The Hive          0207924 6233
*Lovely shop in Battersea, South London selling honey*
*and equipment. Also runs beekeeping courses.*

### Plants and Seeds for Bees

The Beth Chatto Gardens          01206 822007
*Catalogue has good list of perennial plants loved by bees.*
Sarah Raven's Cutting Garden          01424 838181
*Seeds of annual flowers for cutting - many good for bees.*
Suffolk Herbs          01376 572456
*Seeds of herbs, cottage garden flowers and green manures.*

### Books to Read

Honey, by Sue Style          Pavilion
*(wide ranging on bees, honey and recipes).*
A Recipe for Bees, by Gail Anderson-Dargatz          Virago
*(lyrical novel about a Canadian woman beekeeper).*
Honey Bees - a Guide to Management, by Ron Brown
*(precise guide with illustrations from the Crowood Press).*

The British Beekeepers' Association publishes a number
of advisory leaflets.          02476 696679